100 YEARS OF POPULA

PIANO/VOCAL/CHORDS

Series Editor:
Carol Cuellar

Editorial and Production:
Artemis Music Limited

Design and Production:
JPCreativeGroup.com

Published 2003

International
MUSIC
Publications

International Music Publications Limited
Griffin House 161 Hammersmith Road London W6 8BS England

CONTENTS

80s

In the aftermath of World War II, as the 20th Century approached its mid-point, the dying author George Orwell retreated to an isolated house on the Hebridean island of Jura to complete his novel *Nineteen Eighty-Four*. The great writer had envisioned a very different world when he looked to that distant year, and in a sense his prediction held true.

Much about the world had changed in the 35 years that elapsed from 1949, when Orwell published his futuristic work, to 1984 – but "Big Brother", the "Thought Police", and the other horrors of totalitarianism that he warned about had not crushed the human spirit. On the contrary, it was the unprecedented level of freedom, openness, and tolerance that made the real world of 1984 so different from the grim facts of life in Orwell's day.

When Orwell laboured on his book, the city of Berlin had just been divided between the communist east and democratic west. Yet, when the year 1984 actually arrived, the Berlin Wall, which had come to symbolise not only the division of a city but of two worlds, had already shown the deep fissures that ultimately led to its fall by the end of the decade.

As Orwell struggled against the tuberculosis that would eventually overtake him, the US and Soviet Union were just beginning a perilous cycle that would later be called "the nuclear arms race". By the time our

calendars reached 1984, however, this dangerous spiral had begun to slow down, thanks to a series of treaties, one of which would mandate the dismantling of over 2,600 nuclear missile warheads in 1987.

Indeed, it's safe to suggest that in 1984, the world was freer, more democratic, and more peaceful than it had ever been in Orwell's 47-year life. Totalitarianism, the scourge of the 20th Century, had finally begun to wane in the '80s. At the start of the decade, Polish labour leader Lech Walesa led a successful strike at the Lenin Shipyards in Gdansk, setting in motion a series of events that would unravel the Soviet Union's hold on his country. In Russia itself, Mikhail Gorbachev's policies of glasnost and perestroika ushered in a new era of reform that would ultimately lead to the end of the one-party communist state, and of the Cold War.

Meanwhile, in the West, the '80s saw the abatement of old prohibitions, as society became more open and tolerant. Relations between different races grew more congenial-- though there was still much progress to be made--and women assumed a more equal role in business, government, and every other phase of life. Prime Minister Margaret Thatcher inspired strong feelings amongst those who admired and opposed her, but no one could dispute the fact that the ascent of this tough, strong-willed woman was a seminal moment in her gender's history.

Music For A Shrinking World

The democratic changes that took place in the '80s, combined with rapid advances in communications, created a sense of universal understanding that is evident in the decade's music. An excellent example of this is the 1984 hit, "Do They Know It's Christmas?".

Written by Irish punk/new wave rocker Bob Geldof to aid the starving children of Africa, this Christmas benefit song became the best-selling single in the history of Britain. "Do They Know It's Christmas?" was performed by Band Aid, a group made up of many of the UK's biggest rock stars that came together just to record the song. A 16-hour follow-up Live Aid concert held in 1985 was beamed to over 150 countries on television to raise added funds for African famine victims.

Geldof, who was later nominated for the Nobel Peace Prize and knighted by Queen Elizabeth, was inspired to begin his charity campaign after seeing a BBC documentary on the famine in Ethiopia. His experience was indicative of how television helped bring people from different parts of the world closer in the '80s. The advent of cable television news made distant events, from protests in Tiananmen Square to civil wars in Africa, seem as if they were taking place next door. This intimacy encouraged people to develop a more global perspective, which was reflected in popular music. Many of the hits of the '80s fused musical influences from different cultures to create their own unique sound. "Japanese Boy", the 1981 hit from Aneka, lent an unmistakable Asian twist to a catchy blend of disco rhythms and synthesized sounds. The singer Nena and her self-named group had a multi-national hit in the mid-80s with the anti-nuclear anthem "99 Red Balloons", a song that mixed German and English lyrics, as well as folk and new wave musical styles.

The Irish artist Enya fused folk and Celtic music with new age influences to create one of the most distinctive musical styles of the '80s or any decade. Hailing from a musical family – her father Leo Brennan was the leader of the popular Irish group the Slieve Foy Band – Enya began performing professionally while still in her

teens. Later, she went on to pursue a solo career, recording film and television scores.

In 1988, Enya released her *Watermark* album, featuring the beautiful and evocative single "Orinoco Flow", which went on to become a No. 1 hit in the UK. Reflective and soothing, with its flowing music and overdubbed vocals, Enya's *Watermark* album sold over 8 million copies and established her as an international new age star.

As befits a decade known for its spirit of harmony and co-operation, the '80s was a time of great duets. Among the most popular was Michael Jackson and Paul McCartney's 1983 collaboration "The Girl Is Mine". The easy-going ballad, which brought together the most commercially successful songwriter in history with the self-styled "King Of Pop," spanned generations, races, nationalities, and musical styles.

"The Girl Is Mine" was the first of many hits from Michael Jackson's multi-Grammy-winning *Thriller* album. With 40 million copies sold in its initial chart run, *Thriller* became the best-selling album of all time. Covering everything from soft ballads to hard funk, with a mix of synthesized rock and disco thrown in for good measure, *Thriller* provided a sleek showcase for Jackson's diverse talents.

In "Billie Jean", one of the album's biggest hits, Jackson combines a dark and brooding narrative about a paternity dispute with an electrifying disco performance to create a whirlwind of intense and often conflicting emotions. Like many of Jackson's best songs of the decade, "Billie Jean" was an irresistible dance tune, providing an ideal musical platform for the star's famous "moonwalk".

Multi-Media Rock Stars

With his break-dancing moves, single white sequined glove, sunglasses, glitzy apparel, and untied shoes, Jackson presented a stunning and unforgettable image on music videos. His movements, mannerisms, and outfits were studied, copied, and embraced by millions of young people from London to Lagos, creating one of the most vibrant looks of the '80s.

Along with the immensely popular Madonna, Jackson demonstrated the power and importance of the music video as an art form and cultural force in the early and mid '80s. In the hands of the right artist, a video not only contributed to the commercial success of a hit tune, it also worked with the music to bring a new perspective on the emotional and creative forces behind the song.

Like Jackson, Madonna relied on stunning choreography, brilliant production effects, and dramatic, often provocative, narratives to create music videos that captivated audiences. This was very evident in the video for her hit "Papa Don't Preach", which, like "Billie Jean", dealt with the subject of teenage pregnancy, but this time from the girl's perspective.

The American-born artist Prince equalled Jackson and Madonna in influence as a multi-media star throughout much of the '80s. An inspired composer and performer, Prince demonstrated a remarkable genius for balancing opposing emotions and conflicting images in his distinctive brand of psychedelic tinged funk/rock music. In songs like "1999" and "Purple Rain", Prince manages to be raw and eloquent, brash and fragile. Other artists also had hits with Prince's music during the '80s. His carefree song "Manic Monday" reached No.2 on the UK and US charts for the American female quartet, The Bangles.

George Michael and Andrew Ridgeley used exciting and controversial music videos to help make their duo Wham! the most commercially successful British pop group of the '80s. Moving from slow ballads, to rap, to up-tempo songs, Wham! covered a broad musical landscape. Their ebullient breakthrough hit,

"Wake Me Up Before You Go-Go" reached No. 1 on the UK charts in 1984. It was quickly followed by the hit "Careless Whisper", a troubling ballad about infidelity, which gave Ridgeley credit for his role in writing the song, but named Michael as the lead singer. This distinction foreshadowed the eventual break-up of Wham! In June 1986, the group performed a farewell concert before 72,000 fans at Wembley Stadium.

Of course, not all of the stars that shined on the multi-media stage of the '80s were newcomers. Music videos also proved to be a welcome new challenge for some of rock's most venerable names. Elton John, whose fantastic career was in danger of losing momentum at the start of the decade, had one of the best-selling hits of 1983 with the album *Too Low For Zero*. This album was jump-started by the popularity of John's song and music video "I'm Still Standing".

Confident, triumphant, and optimistic, "I'm Still Standing" was a fitting song for John, who had overcome adversity to regain his artistic voice, as well as for the wonderful decade of the '80s – a time when the world seemed to have learned from the past and was ready to leap into the future with the élan of a video dancer.

Ten Things That First Appeared In The '80s

1. **Laptop computer.**
2. **Big screen TV.**
3. **Panini football stickers.**
4. **Disposable cameras.**
5. **Phone cards.**
6. **CD players.**
7. **BBC's *Breakfast Time*.**
8. **Microsoft Windows operating system.**
9. **Care Bears.**
10. **Leg warmers.**

ABSOLUTE BEGINNERS

Words and Music by DAVID BOWIE

11

ALL AT ONCE

Words by JEFFREY OSBORNE and MICHAEL MASSER
Music by MICHAEL MASSER

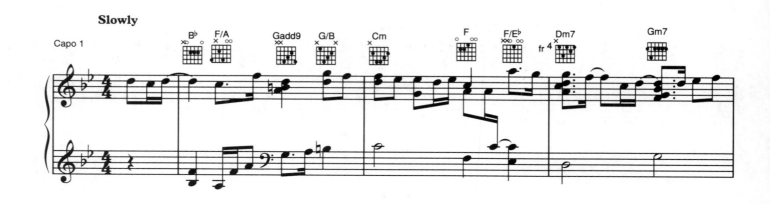

All at once

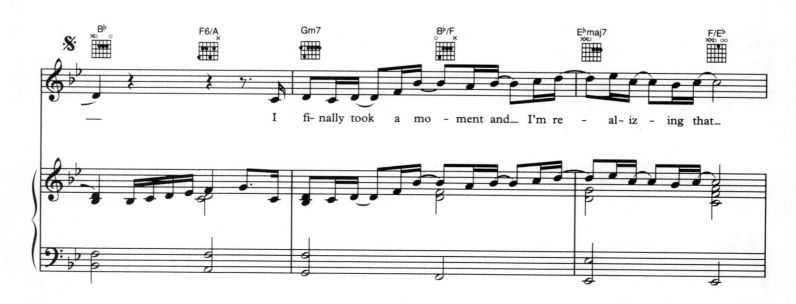

I fi-nally took a mo-ment and_ I'm re - al - iz - ing that_

Verse 2:
All at once
I looked around and found
That you were with another love
In someone else's arms
And all my dreams were shattered
All at once

All at once
The smile that used to greet me
Brightens someone else's day
She took your smile away
And left me with just memories
All at once

ALWAYS

Words and Music by JOHN LEWIS, DAVID LEWIS
and WAYNE LEWIS

ANYTHING FOR YOU

Words and Music by GLORIA ESTEFAN

CALL ME

Words and Music by
DEBORAH HARRY and GIORGIO MORODER

Moderate Rock shuffle

BABOOSHKA

Words and Music by KATE BUSH

Moderately

Capo 1

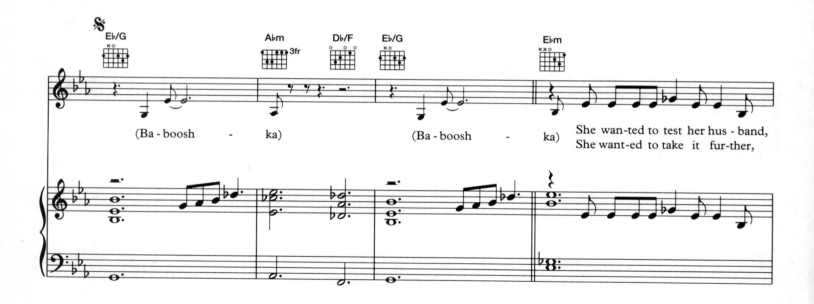

(Ba - boosh - ka)   (Ba - boosh - ka)   She wan-ted to test her hus - band,
                                             She want-ed to take it fur-ther,

she knew ex - act - ly what to do,   a pseu-do-nym___ to fool him,___
so she ar-ranged a place to go,   for to see___ if he___

BABY COME TO ME

Words and Music by ROD TEMPERTON

Verse 2:
Spendin' every dime to keep you talkin' on the line
That's how it was
And all those walks together
Out in any kind of weather
Just because
There's a brand new way of looking at your life
When you know that love is standing by your side

BEING WITH YOU

Words and Music by WILLIAM ROBINSON

*Optional repeat of 8 bars Intro. (Instr. solo) before 2nd Verse.

BILLIE JEAN

Words and Music by MICHAEL JACKSON

BREAKOUT

Words and Music by ANDREW CONNELL, CORINNE DREWERY
and MARTIN JACKSON

- pla - na - tions make no sense when ev - ery ans-wer's wrong.
- tu - a - tions ne - ver change to mor - row looks un - sure.

You're fight - ing with lost con - fi-dence all ex-
Don't leave your des - ti - ny to chance what are

- pec - ta - tions gone the time has come to make
you wait - ing for? The time has come to make

D.%. and fade

CAN'T STAY AWAY FROM YOU

Words and Music by GLORIA ESTEFAN

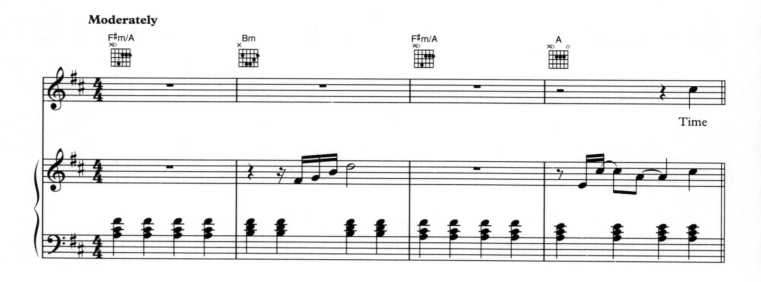

Time

flies   when you're hav – ing fun,   I heard some – bo – dy say.
on   to   ev – ery bit of hope,   that's all I ev – er do,

But if all I've been is fun,   then ba – by, let me go.   Don't wan – na be in your
hop – ing you might change your mind   and call me up to say   how much you need me

CARELESS WHISPER

Words and Music by
GEORGE MICHAEL and ANDREW RIDGELEY

Slow Ballad

1. I feel so___ un - sure___ as I
2. Time can ne - ver mend___ the
3. (To) - night the music seems so loud, I wish that we could lose this crowd,

take your hand___ and lead you to the dance floor;
care - less whis - per of a good friend;
may - be it's bet - ter this way, if we'd hurt each oth - er with the things we want to say.___ We

DO THEY KNOW IT'S CHRISTMAS?

Words and Music by
MIDGE URE and BOB GELDOF

CAUGHT UP IN THE RAPTURE

Words and Music by DIANNE QUANDER and GARRY DE WAYNE GLENN

When we met_____ al - ways_____ knew, I would feel_____
We stand_____ side by_____ side,_ 'til the storms

_____ that mag - ic for you._____ On my mind,_____ con - stant-
_____ of life_____ pass us by._____ Light my fire,_____ warm my

CHARIOTS OF FIRE

Composed by VANGELIS

EMI Music Publishing Ltd, London WC2H 0EA

COME ON EILEEN

Words and Music by KEVIN ROWLAND,
KEVIN ADAMS and JIM PATTERSON

Come on__ Ei-leen.

1. Poor old John-ny Ray_____ sound-ed sad up-on__ the ra - di - o;__ he moved a
2. These peo - ple round here_____ wear beat - en down eyes, sunk in smoke dried fa - ces; re-

71

DON'T YOU WANT ME

Words and Music by PHILIP OAKEY, ADRIAN WRIGHT
and JO CALLIS

Moderately

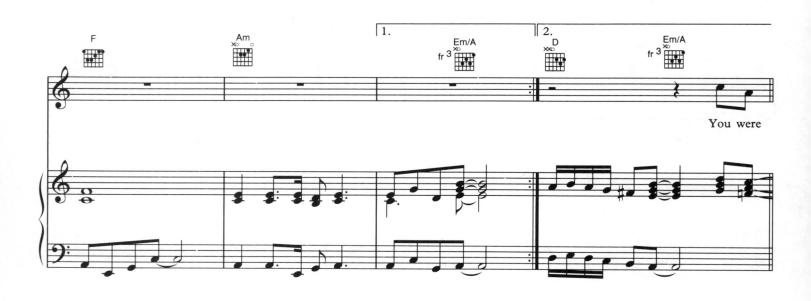

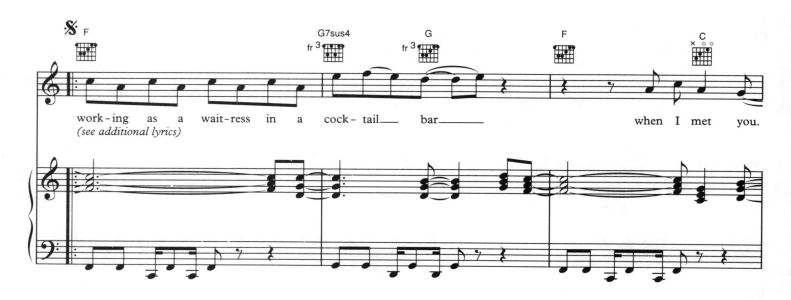

work-ing as a wait-ress in a cock-tail___ bar___ when I met you.
(see additional lyrics)

Don't you want me ba - by,   don't you want me,   oh._____

Verse 2:
Now five years later on you've got the world at your feet
Success has been easy for you
But don't forget it's me who put you where you are now
And I can put you back down too

Verse 3:
I was working as a waitress in a cocktail bar
That much is true
But even then I knew I'd find a much better place
Either with or without you

Verse 4:
The five years we have had have been such good times
I still love you
But now I think it's time I live my life on my own
I guess it's just what I must do

EVERYTHING MUST CHANGE

Words and Music by PAUL YOUNG and IAN KEWLEY

83

84

FOR YOUR EYES ONLY

Words by MICHAEL LEESON
Music by BILL CONTI

EYE OF THE TIGER

Words and Music by
FRANKIE SULLIVAN III and JIM PETERIK

FAME

Words by DEAN PITCHFORD
Music by MICHAEL GORE

FRIENDS WILL BE FRIENDS

Words and Music by FREDDIE MERCURY and JOHN DEACON

An-oth-er red let-ter day. So the pound has dropped and the child-ren are cre-a-ting.
Now it's a beau-ti-ful day. The post-man de-li-vered a let-ter from your lov-er.
3. Instr.

The oth-er half ran a-way, tak-ing all the cash and leav-ing you with the lum-ber.
On-ly a phone-call a-way. He tried to track him down but some-bo-dy stole his num-ber.

out your hand,'cause (1.2.)friends will be friends,_____ right to the end.__

(3.) right to the end,_____

right to the end.__

right to the end.__

THE GIRL IS MINE

Words and Music by MICHAEL JACKSON

HAPPY BIRTHDAY

Words and Music by STEVIE WONDER

birth - day, _____ hap-py birth - day. _____ Hap - py

Verse 2:
I just never understood
How a man who died for good
Could not have a day that would
Be set aside for his recognition
Because it should never be
Just because some cannot see
The dream as clear as he
That they should make it become an illusion
And we all know everything
That he stood for time will bring
For in peace our hearts will sing
Thanks to Martin Luther King
Happy birthday . . .

Verse 3:
The time is overdue
For people like me and you
Who know the way to truth
Is love and unity to all God's children
It should be a great event
And the whole day should be spent
In full rememberance
Of those who lived and died
For the oneness of all people
So let us all begin
We know that love can win
Let it out, don't hold it in
Sing as loud as you can
Happy birthday . . .

Recitation for fade ending:
We know the key to unity of all people
It was in the dream that we had so long ago
That lives in all of the hearts of people
That believe in unity
We will make the dream become a reality
I know we will, because our hearts tell us so

HAPPY TALK

Words by OSCAR HAMMERSTEIN II
Music by RICHARD RODGERS

Gracefully

Hap - py talk, keep talk - in' hap - py talk,_____

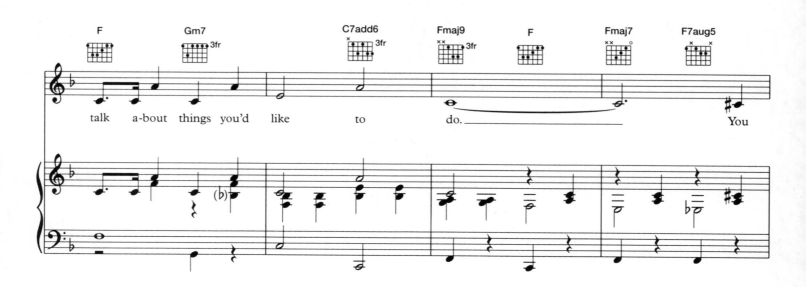

talk a-bout things you'd like to do._____ You

HOLDING BACK THE YEARS

Words by MICK HUCKNALL
Music by MICK HUCKNALL and NEIL MOSS

Slow Ballad

HEAVEN

Words and Music by BRYAN ADAMS and JIM VALLANCE

And ba-by, you're all___ that I want when you're ly-in' here___ in my arms. I'm

find-ing it hard to be-lieve we're in hea-ven. And love is all___that I need, and I

found it there in your heart. It is-n't too hard to see___ we're in hea-ven, hea-ven.___

HOLDING OUT FOR A HERO

Words by DEAN PITCHFORD
Music by JIM STEINMAN

Up where the moun-tains meet the heav-ens a-bove,__

out where the light-ning splits__ the sea,_____ I could swear there is some-

HOW AM I SUPPOSED TO LIVE WITHOUT YOU?

Words and Music by
MICHAEL BOLTON and DOUG JAMES

Moderately

I could hard-ly bel-ieve_____ it   when I
I'm too proud for cry - in',   did-n't

heard the news to-day,   I had to come and set it straight from you.
come here to__ break-down.   It's just a dream of mine is com-ing to__ an end.

I AM WHAT I AM

Words and Music by JERRY HERMAN

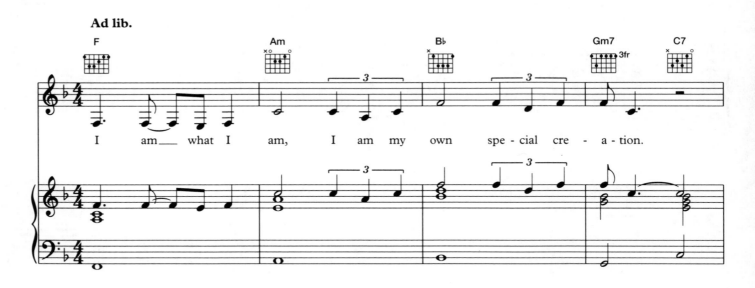

I am __ what I am, I am my own spe- cial cre- a- tion.

So come, take a look, give me the hook or the o- va- tion. It's my

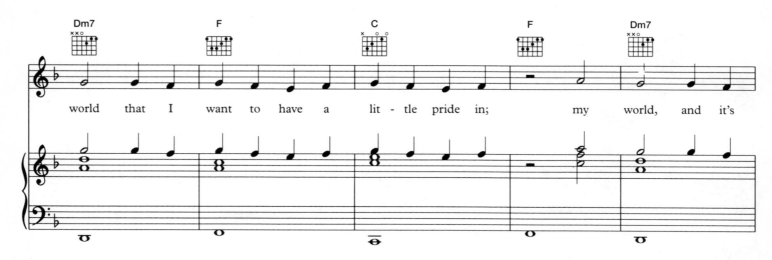

world that I want to have a lit- tle pride in; my world, and it's

I'M STILL STANDING

Words and Music by
ELTON JOHN and BERNIE TAUPIN

3   Once I never could hope to win
    You starting down the road
    Leaving me again. The Threats
    You made were meant to cut me down
    And if our love was just a circus
    You'd be a clown by now

I DON'T WANNA DANCE

Words and Music by EDDY GRANT

I don't wan-na dance, dance with you, ba-by no____ more.____ I'll

ne - ver do some-thing to hurt you, though oh, but the feel - ing is bad, the feel - ing is

bad.

I love your per - so - na - li-ty oh but I don't want our love on
Ba - by now the par-ty's ov - er____ for us, so I'll be on my

I SHOULD HAVE KNOWN BETTER

Words and Music by JIM DIAMOND and GRAHAM LYLE

149

I WANT TO BREAK FREE

Words and Music by JOHN DEACON

153

I WON'T LET THE SUN GO DOWN ON ME

Words and Music by NICHOLAS KERSHAW

159

I'M SO EXCITED

Words and Music by ANITA POINTER,
RUTH POINTER, JUNE POINTER and TREVOR LAWRENCE

1. To-night's_ the night we're gon - na make it hap-
(2.) should-n't ev - en think_ a - bout to-mor-

(Instrumental)

- pen,
- row,

to - night_ we'll put_ all oth - er things a - side.
sweet mem - or - ies_ will last a long,_ long time.

Give in___ this time_ and show me some af - fec-
We'll have___ a good_ time ba - by don't you wor-

161

163

IF I COULD TURN BACK TIME

Words and Music by DIANE WARREN

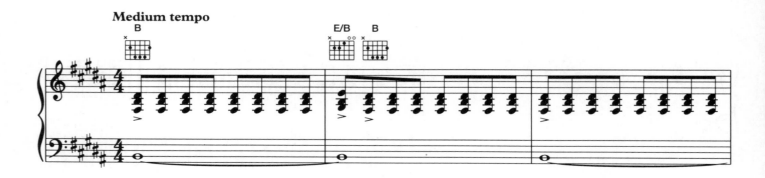

If I could turn ___ back time, if I could find ___ a ___ way,

I'd take back ___ those words that-'ve hurt ___ you and you'd stay.

IS THIS LOVE?

Words and Music by
DAVID COVERDALE and JOHN SYKES

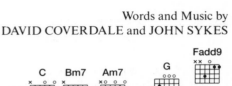

Slow Rock

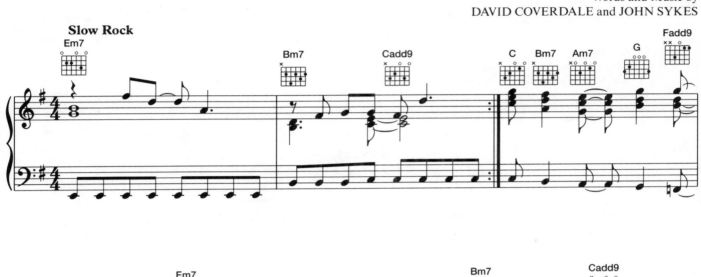

I should have known bet-ter than to let you go a-lone,
I find I spend my time wait-ing on your call,
I can't stop the feeling I've been this way be-fore,

it's times like these I can't make it on my own,
how can I tell you babe, my back's a-gainst the wall.
but with you I've found the key to op-en a-ny door.

wast-ed days___ and sleep - less nights,____ and I can't wait to see_ you a - gain.
I need you by my side to tell me it's all right,__ 'cause I
I can feel my love for you growing strong-er day by day___ and

to Coda ⊕

2.

don't think I can take a - ny - more.___ Is this love

Chorus

that I'm feel - ing, is this the love____ that I've been

JAPANESE BOY

Words and Music by BOB HEATLIE

He said that he loved me,— ne-ver would go,— oh, oh,— oh, oh.—
Peo-ple ask a-bout him,— ev-e-ry day, oh, oh,— oh, oh.—

Now I find I'm sit - ting_ here on my own, oh, oh,— oh, oh.— Was it some-thing
Don't know what to tell_ them, what can I say,— oh, oh,— oh, oh.— If on-ly he would

173

KEEP ON LOVING YOU

Words and Music by KEVIN CRONIN

Moderately

You should have seen by the look in my eyes,— ba - by, there was some - thin' miss-in.'

You should have known by the tone of my voice, may - be,

but you did - n't lis - ten.— You played dead, but you ne - ver bled. In-

KIDS IN AMERICA

Words and Music by MARTY WILDE and RICKY WILDE

ev – ery – where.   I don't__ want__ to go, ba – by.

New York to East__ Ca – li – for – nia   there's a new wave com – ing, I warn you.

D.%· al Coda

CODA

We're the kids,   we're the kids,   we're the kids in A – me – ri – ca.__

repeat and fade

THE KING OF ROCK 'N' ROLL

Words and Music by PADDY McALOON

Verse 2:
The dream helps you forget
You ain't never danced a step
You were never fleet of foot
Hippy
All the pathos you can keep
For the children in the street
For the vision I have had
Is weeping
New broom, this room
Sweep it clean

Verse 3:
Now my rhythm ain't so hot
But it's the only friend I've got
I'm the king of rock and roll
Completely
All the pretty birds have flown
Now I'm dancing on my own
I'm the king of rock and roll
Completely
Up from suede shoes
To my baby blues

LAND OF MAKE BELIEVE

Words and Music by ANDY HILL and PETE SINFIELD

Stars in your eyes, lit-tle one, where do you go to dream?

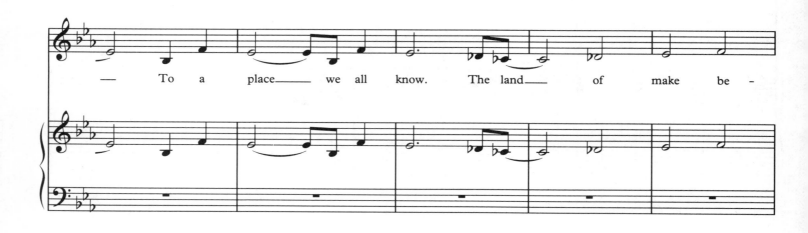

To a place we all know. The land of make be-

-lieve.

191

MANIC MONDAY

Words and Music by CHRISTOPHER

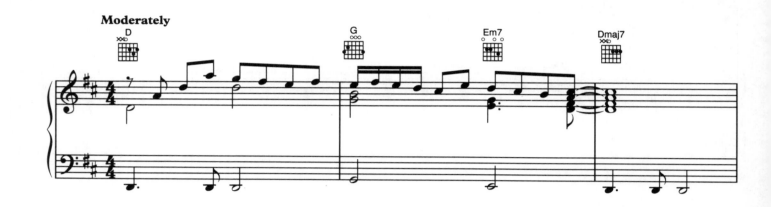

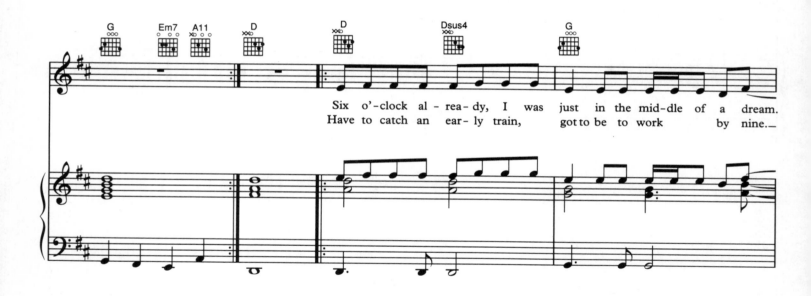

Six o'-clock al-rea-dy, I was just in the mid-dle of a dream.
Have to catch an ear-ly train, got to be to work by nine.—

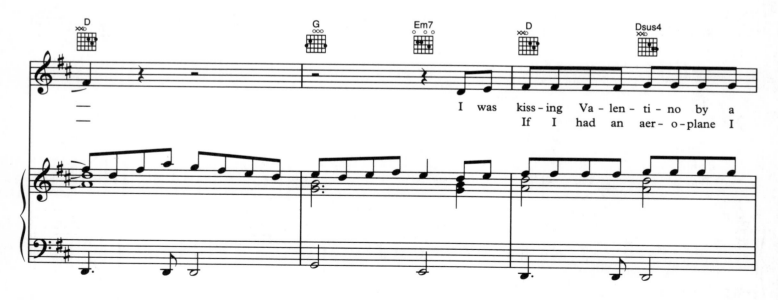

— I was kiss-ing Va-len-ti-no by a
— If I had an aer-o-plane I

198

MISS YOU LIKE CRAZY

Words and Music by PRESTON GLASS,
MICHAEL MASSER and GERRY GOFFIN

Slowly

1. E - ven though it's been_ so long,_ my love for you_ keeps

go - ing strong. I re - mem - ber the things that we used to do, a kiss in the rain till the sun shined through. I

203

Just one night, and we'll have___ to find the feel-ings like we used to do.___

Hold on tight, and what-ev - er comes our way, we're gon-na make it through._____ It

205

MISSING YOU

Words and Music by JOHN WAITE, MARK LEONARD
and CHAS SANDFORD

Medium rock

Ev- ery time I think of you, I al - ways catch my breath,
name in cer - tain cir - cles, and it al - ways makes me smile.
know how des - perate I've be - come and it looks like I'm los - ing this fight.

— and I'm still stand-ing here, and you're miles a - way, and I'm
— I spend my time think - ing a - bout you, and it's
— In your world I have no mean - ing, though I'm

MY ONE TEMPTATION

Words and Music by MICK LEESON, PETER VALE
and MILES WATERS

212

1.

you're my one temp - ta - tion. You can look

2.

Gᵇmaj7

you're my one temp - ta - tion.

Dm7　　　　　Gm7 fr 3　　　　　Dm7　　　　　Gm7 fr 3

Eᵇmaj7　　　　　F

No - thing ev - er hap - pens 'til you

A NEW FLAME

Words and Music by MICK HUCKNALL

219

NINE TO FIVE

Words and Music by DOLLY PARTON

Tum-ble out of bed and stum-ble to the kitch - en; pour my-self a cup___ of am - bi-tion, and
(see additional lyrics)

yawn, and stretch, and try to come_ to life.___

Jump in the show-er and the blood stars pump-ing; out on the street, the traf - fic starts jump-ing, with folks

1.3.4.5.6. *to fade* | **2.**

D7   D7

cra - zy, if___ you let it.   out___ to get___ me.

G   N.C.   *D. %*

2. They

Verse 2:
They let you dream just to watch them shatter
You're just a step on the boss man's ladder
But you've got dreams he'll never take away
In the same boat with a lot of your friends
Waitin' for the day your ship'll come in
And the tide's gonna turn, and it's all gonna roll your way

Chorus 4 & 6:
Nine to five, they've got you where they want you
There's a better life, and you dream about it, don't you
It's a rich man's game, no matter what they call it
And you spend your life putting money in his pocket

99 RED BALLOONS

Words and Music by JORN-UWE FAHRENKROG-PETERSEN and CARLO KARGES
English Lyrics by KEVIN McALEA

Edition Hate GmbH and EMI Songs Musikverlag GmbH, Germany
EMI Songs Ltd, London WC2H 0EA

Nine - ty nine__ red bal - loons__ float - ing in the sum -
Nine - ty nine__ de - ci - sion street, nine - ty nine min - is -
Nine - ty nine__ knights of the air__ ride su - per high - tech jet__

ON THE BEACH

Words and Music by CHRISTOPHER ANTON REA

2   The secrets of the summer I will keep
    The sands of time will blow a mystery
    No one but you and I
    Underneath that moonlit sky
    Take me back to the place that I know
    On the beach

ON THE WINGS OF LOVE

Words by JEFFREY OSBORNE
Music by PETER SCHLESS

Just smile for me and let the day be- gin.
(see additional lyrics)

You are the sun- shine that lights my heart with - in. And I'm sure that you're an an-

- gel in dis- guise. Come take my hand and to - ge-ther we will ride.

1st time only

236

fly-ing high up-on— the wings of love,_____

of_____ love._____

Verse 2:
You look at me and I begin to melt
Just like the snow, when a ray of sun is felt
And I'm crazy 'bout you, baby, can't you see?
I'd be so delighted if you would come with me

ORINOCO FLOW

Words and Music by ENYA, NICKY RYAN
and ROMA RYAN

repeat and fade

- way.—
    sail,— we can sail,— sail a – way, sail a – way, sail a – way.   Sail a -

Verse 2:
From Bissau to Palau in the shade of Avalon
From Fiji to Tiree and the Isles of Ebony
From Peru to Cebu, feel the power of Babylon
From Bali to Cali far beneath the Coral Sea

Verse 3:
From the North to the South, Ebudae unto Khartoum
From the deep Sea of Clouds to the Island of the Moon
Carry me on the waves to the lands I've never been
Carry me on the waves to the lands I've never seen

ONE MOMENT IN TIME

Words and Music by JOHN BETTIS and ALBERT HAMMOND

PAPA DON'T PREACH

Words and Music by BRIAN ELLIOT
Additional Lyrics by MADONNA CICCONE

PIANO IN THE DARK

Words and Music by BRENDA RUSSELL,
JEFF HULL and SCOTT CUTLER

THE POWER OF LOVE

Words by JENNIFER RUSH and MARY SUSAN APPLEGATE
Music by CANDY DE ROUGE and GUNTHER MENDE

The whis-pers___ in the morn-ing___ of lov-ers sleep-ing tight,

are roll-ing by loke thun-der now as I look in your eyes.

I hold on to your bo-dy,___ and feel each move you
times,_____ it seems I'm far a-

SAVE A PRAYER

Words and Music by SIMON LE BON, ANDY TAYLOR, ROGER TAYLOR
JOHN TAYLOR and NICK RHODES

You saw me stand-ing by the wall cor-ner of a main street,
Feel the breeze deep on the in-side, look you down in-to the

and the lights are flash-ing on your win-dow sill.
well. If you can you'll see the world in all his fire.

SEE THE DAY

Words and Music by D C LEE

SHE'S LIKE THE WIND

Words and Music by PATRICK SWAYZE and STACY WIDELITZ

She's like the wind through my tree.

She rides the night next to me. She

leads me through moon-light on-ly to burn me with the sun. She's

I

look in the mir – ror   and all I see___   is a

young old man___   with on–ly a dream.   Am I just

fool – ing my–self___   that she'll stop the pain?

SUPERWOMAN

Words and Music by ANTONIO REID, KENNY EDMONDS
and DARYL SIMMONS

Early in the morning I put breakfast at your table, and
say the juice is sour it used to be so sweet, and I
way through the rush hour trying to make it home just for you, I want to
think I am just crazy when I say that you've changed, I'm con-

make sure that your coffee has its sugar and cream,— your—
can't help but to wonder if you're talking 'bout be,— we don't
make sure that your dinner will be waiting for you,— but when you
-vinced I know the problem, you don't love me the same,— you're just

ST ELMO'S FIRE (MAN IN MOTION)

Words and Music by DAVID FOSTER and JOHN PARR

279

repeat ad lib. and fade

All I need is a pair of wheels. Take me where the fu-ture's ly-ing; St. El-mo's Fire.___

Verse 2:

Play the game; you know you can't quit until it's won
Soldier on, only you can do what must be done
You know, in some ways you're a lot like me
You're just a prisoner, and you're tryin' to break free

Verse 3:

Burning up; don't know just how far that I can go
Soon be home; only just a few miles down the road
And I can make it, I know I can
You broke the boy in me, but you won't break the man

Chorus 3:

I can hear the music playin'; I can see the banners fly
Feel like a vet again. I hope I ain't high
Gonna be your man in motion; all I need is a pair of wheels
Take me where the future's lying; St. Elmo's fire

TAINTED LOVE

Words and Music by ED COBB

TELL ME THERE'S A HEAVEN

Words and Music by CHRIS REA

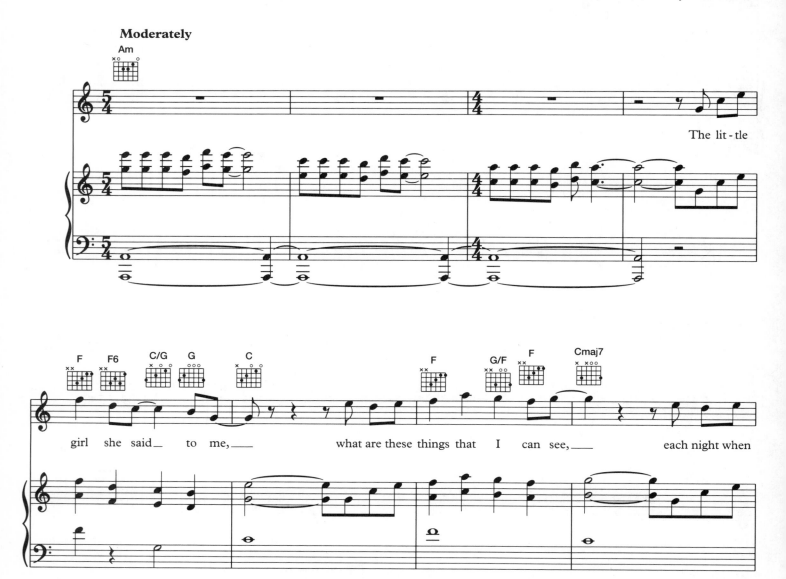

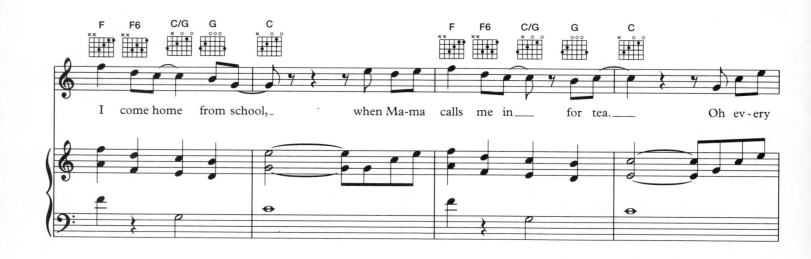

TOTAL ECLIPSE OF THE HEART

Words and Music by JIM STEINMAN

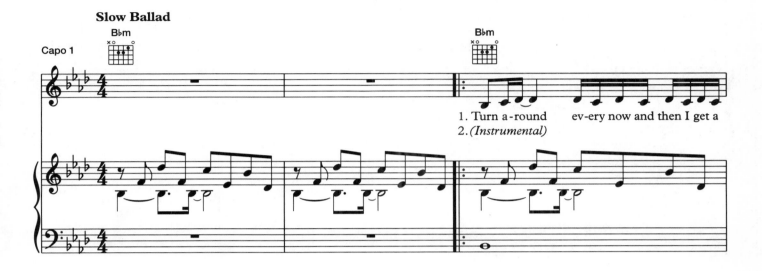

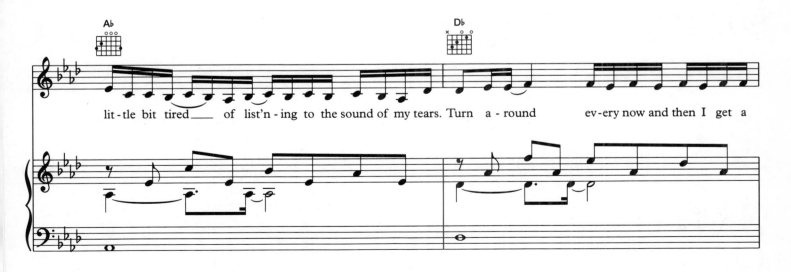

(I'VE HAD) THE TIME OF MY LIFE

Words and Music by FRANKIE PREVITE,
JOHN DE NICOLA and DONALD MARKOWITZ

UPSIDE DOWN

Words and Music by BERNARD EDWARDS and NILE RODGERS

307

say to thee re-spect-ful-ly.— Up-side down you're turn-in' me.—

repeat to fade

A VIEW TO A KILL

Words and Music by
DURAN DURAN and JOHN BARRY

2 Choice for you is the view to a kill
Between the shades, assassination standing still
The first crystal tears
Fall in snowflakes in your body
First time in years
To drench you skin with lovers' rosy stain
A chance to find a phoenix for the flame
A chance to die, but can we

(*To Chorus*)

WAKE ME UP BEFORE YOU GO-GO

Words and Music by GEORGE MICHÆL

YOU BRING ME JOY

Words and Music by DAVID LASLEY

You bring me_____ joy_____ when I'm down. Oh, so much joy._____ When I lose my way, your love comes smil-ing on me._____ I saw your face, (see additional lyrics) and then I knew we would be_____ friends._____ I was

When I lose my way, your love comes smil-ing on me.

Verse 2:
You bring me joy
Don't go too far away
If I can't see your face, I will remember that smile

But can this be right
Or should we be friends?
I get lonely sometimes and I'm mixed up again
'Cause you're the best I've seen in all my life
You bring me joy
My joy, my joy

Verse3:
I believe this is gonna be what you want it to be
I just love you, I just love you, can't you see
That you're the best I've seen in all my life
You bring me joy

WALKING ON SUNSHINE

Words and Music by KIMBERLEY REW

ZOOM

330

Words and Music by
LEN BARRY and BOBBY ELI

100 YEARS OF POPULAR MUSIC

9816A

Vol. 1 - 9817A

Vol. 2 - 9818A

Vol. 1 - 9819A

Vol. 2 - 9820A

International Music
Publications Limited

Vol. 1 - 9821A

Vol. 2 - 9822A

Vol. 1 - 9823A

Vol. 2 - 9824A

Vol. 1 - 9825A

Vol. 2 - 9826A

Vol. 1 - 9827A

Vol. 2 - 9828A

Vol. 1 - 9829A

Vol. 2 - 9830A

Vol. 1 - 9831A

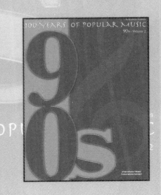

Vol. 2 - 9832A

9833A

IMP
International
MUSIC
Publications

IMP's Exciting New Series!

100 YEARS OF POPULAR MUSIC

IMP
International
MUSIC
Publications

IMP's Exciting New Series!

100 YEARS OF POPULAR MUSIC

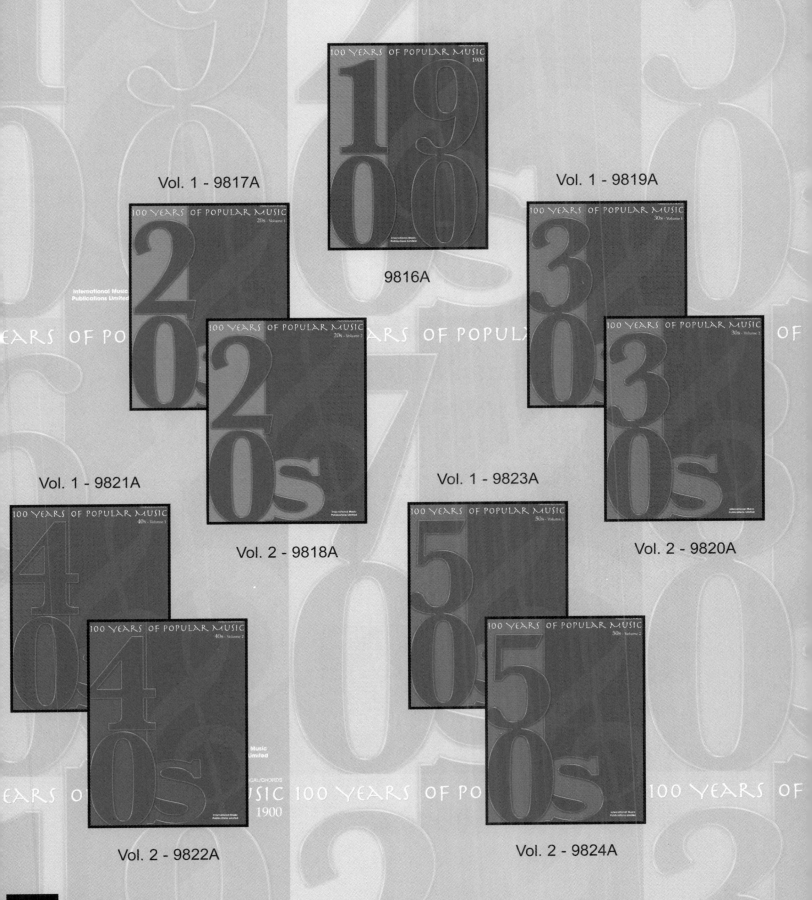

Vol. 1 - 9817A

9816A

Vol. 1 - 9819A

Vol. 1 - 9821A

Vol. 2 - 9818A

Vol. 1 - 9823A

Vol. 2 - 9820A

Vol. 2 - 9822A

Vol. 2 - 9824A

IMP
International
MUSIC
Publications

IMP's Exciting New Series!

100 YEARS OF POPULAR MUSIC

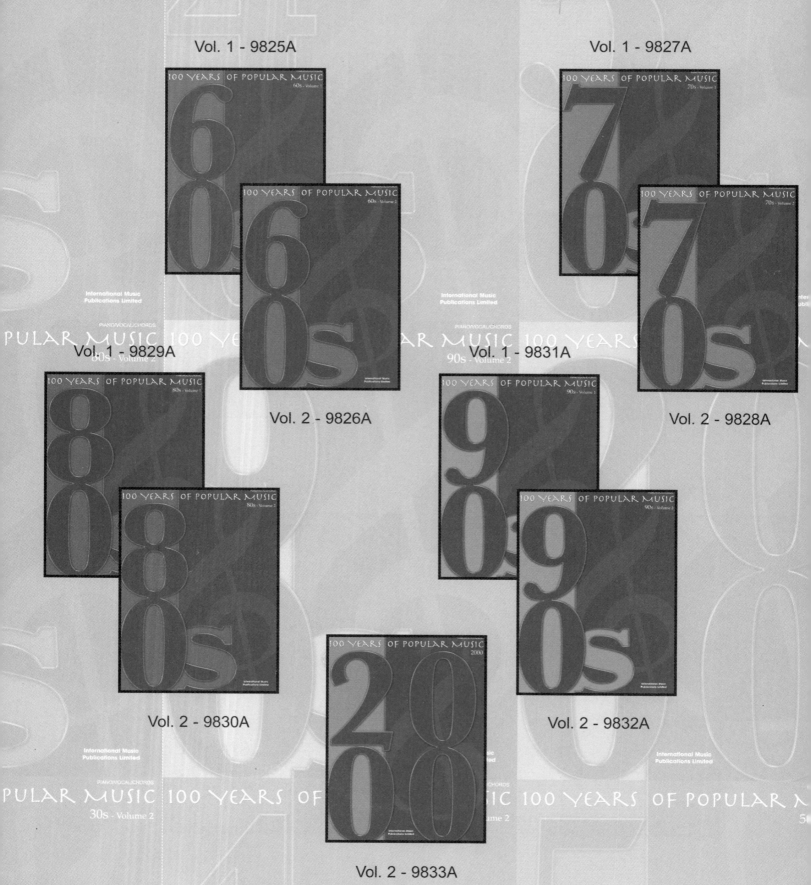

Vol. 1 - 9825A

Vol. 1 - 9827A

Vol. 1 - 9829A

Vol. 1 - 9831A

Vol. 2 - 9826A

Vol. 2 - 9828A

Vol. 2 - 9830A

Vol. 2 - 9832A

Vol. 2 - 9833A

International
MUSIC
Publications

IMP's Exciting New Series!